The Christmas Parrot

Tom Carr

Illustrated by Colin Smithson

THE PARROT PRESS

Among the illuminated Christmas decorations at Richmond in Yorkshire is a large, brightly coloured plastic parrot.
Purchased second-hand some years ago from Blackpool Corporation, it was received at first with some incredulity but is now regarded affectionately as part of the Christmas scene.

Story 1

The Parrot's back Mummy! The Parrot's here,
The Christmas Parrot!" "Bless my soul, she's right!
She must remember from a year ago.
We only saw it once, on Christmas Eve - The Snowman,
Three toy Soldiers, Santa Claus and that huge Parrot,
Yellow, red and blue stuck in a tree, and round him strings of lights,
Bright coloured bulbs hanging from branch to branch."
Jim said "Look out! That parrot'll be down
In all this wind. I don't know why they want
A flaming bird like this at Christmas time.
It isn't right." "Give up!" I said, "you know
She likes it, and I bet she'll always think
That parrots go with Christmas. Let her be.
Come on! We can't stand gaping here all night.
Let's go and find a torch for Uncle Fred."
The Parrot smiled, or tried to, but his face
Was thick with paint that fixed his eyes so tight
They could not move, so all that happened was
A little quiver deep inside his frame
That brought a momentary brighter glow.

He felt the current coursing through his wires
And thought of how his parrot life began — a boiling liquid mass.
A plastic sea from which he rose, congealing on the great
Matrix and Parrot-Father of them all.
The days of naked anonymity
Before the paint-shop gave his feathers life.
Then sounds of laughing children, rolling waves,
The heat of summer suns, the welcome shade
Of the deep ersatz jungle on the beach,
And the long, warm, illuminated nights
When people in their thousands came to see their brightness.
Buses cruised along the front and thirsty trippers
Drank their cans of beer and left them on the concrete forest floor.
Was it a happy time? He could not tell. For then he knew no other,
And to him the trees were trees, and all the plastic birds
Were true to their own form, as he to his.
The alligator lazing in the pool
Remained all day in concrete indolence,
But that was surely what his maker planned
Or what the District Council specified.

Then came the day the foreman brought his men
And stood and looked at all the forest scene
And nodded, "Yes, I thought so. There'll be room
For Star Wars in this comer. That will suit
The youngsters better. All this lot can go."
Switched off. No tears - no tantrums - no regrets.
They went in dim compliance to the sale.
"Lot twenty-three. A mixture - Santa Claus,
A snowman, three toy soldiers, and a bird; a parrot - all
his mates have gone to Crewe.
Missed his connection, this one! Never mind,
They'll get on well enough. What am I bid?
A hundred? Ninety-five? - - - Right Sir - they're yours.
You have a truck? I think you'll find you've got
A bargain! Just be careful with his tail."

And so he came to Richmond, to the Park,
With trees that grew, and changed and shed their leaves.
But first a summer in the Council store
In disconnected somnolence, no power
Enlightening his perception. Then he felt
The stir of action, hoisted up aloft,
Refreshed by moorland winds, and then at last
Alerted by the throbbing of the mains
As Kenny plugged him in and dropped the switch.

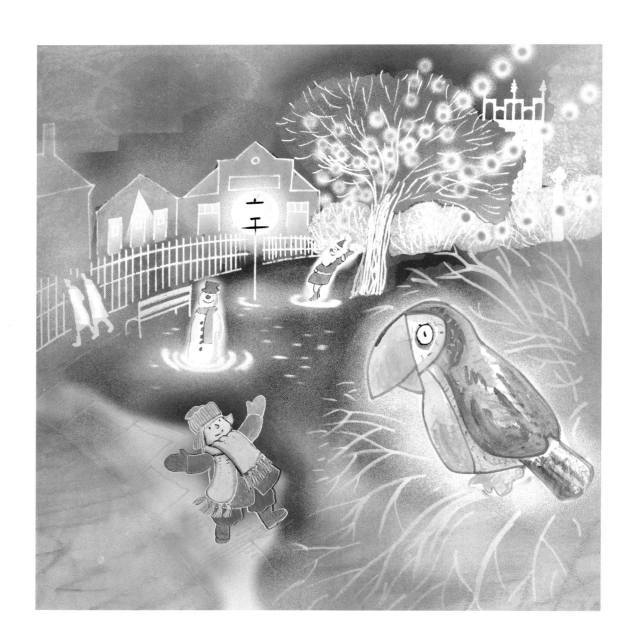

He likes the Park, the trees, the neat trimmed beds,
The people sitting in the winter sun,
The cars and buses, and the lively folk,
Moving around as he can never do.
But when the daylight fails he comes to life
And glows his Christmas message far and wide.
So that the children tug their Mothers' arms,
"Mummy, the Parrot's back, the Parrot's here,
The Richmond Christmas Parrot!"
And he beams
His Christmas happiness
upon the night.

Story 2

Just before Christmas, 1992
The merry merchants of the town came out
To post their Christmas mail
(two days to go!)
Too late of course, and only second class
But they had all been busy at their tills
And office parties. Passing by the Park
They saw the PARROT and his happy friends
Beaming among the rows of shining bulbs.
"What is the purpose of this waste?" they asked
"This is no place to hang the Christmas lights.
They should be round the shops, not in the trees.
We'll see the Mayor at once." So off they went,
leaving their cards to post another year.
These were the merchants and the men of trade
(Not the poor gentle folk like you and me.)
So next year, it was speedily ordained,
"The Christmas Lights shall decorate the Square."

And so indeed it duly came to pass
That Mr Porter (known to us as Ken)
Was sent with ladders, lights, and wire and men,
And trailers, and a quite impressive crane.
Wherewith, despite the snow and hail and rain,
He did the job...
except to find a perch
From which the PARROT
could give light and cheer.

For him there was no room, no home - until
"The Market Cross !"
"We'll use the crane."
"Hold tight!"
They strapped him on,
and up he went aloft.
Higher and higher, till he reached at last
The concrete bubble on the obelisk.
"No good!" said Ken. "You won't get me up there.
Just swing him round
and try him on the Tower."

Our Parrot felt quite sick (as parrots do).
He had no head for heights. He knew his wings
Were quite immobilized. His feathers too
Were just cosmetic, and as he looked down
And saw the tiny figures on the Square
He shuddered. Then the gantry gave a lurch
And dropped him (fairly gently) on the Church.
Ken and his men came running up the stairs.
"All right, old son? Did you enjoy the flight?
Let's see if we can rig you up some light."
He fixed the wires. "O.K. boys. Let it go!"
But all that happened was a faint red glow.
"Bother!" said Ken (or words to that effect)
"You've got a short, somewhere inside, I bet.
I haven't time to fix it now.
Just do your best, young bird. It's very nearly dark."

And there they left him,
Silent, all alone.
No friends, no power,
No room for him below
Among the jolly shoppers in the square.
Consigned to flicker feebly on the roof.
In solitude.

And then he saw the STAR.
Far in the East, a tiny point of light.
But in the darkness it grew firm and bright.
Till a vast brilliance overturned the gloom
And filled our Parrot's heart with happiness
To bursting!
Until he too gleamed and shone with joy.

But no-one heard the quiet voice above,

"When I came down, there was no room for me
So shine for us tonight, shine out dear friend,
Shine out again for all the world to see."

The little girl who said "The Parrot's here!"
Some years ago (now quite a stylish miss - and
Walking out with a good-looking lad)
Looked up and smiled, and gently squeezed his hand,
And said, "The Christmas Parrot's back. I'm glad."